COMMODITY TRADING MANUAL
HOME STUDY WORKBOOK

The information in this publication is taken from sources believed to be reliable, but is not guaranteed by the Chicago Board of Trade as to accuracy, completeness nor any trading result, and is intended only for purposes of information and education. Nothing herein should be considered as a trading recommendation of the Chicago Board of Trade. The Rules and Regulations of the exchange should be consulted as the authoritative source on all current contract specifications and regulations. It might be advisable to consult an attorney regarding legal restrictions in your state applicable to your particular business that might preclude or limit use of futures or options on futures markets.

EM41-3
© Board of Trade of the City of Chicago 1987, 1990
All rights reserved. Printed in the USA.
7.90.10000

TABLE OF CONTENTS

INTRODUCTION

This home study workbook is designed to complement your readings in the *Commodity Trading Manual*. There are six sections, and each one highlights various concepts relating to the futures and options industry. At the end of each section, there are several fill-in and multiple-choice questions to test your futures and options knowledge. You'll also find special practice problems in some of the sections to further improve your understanding of different futures and options concepts.

SECTION ONE—GENERAL INFORMATION

The following highlights cover topics presented in the first seven chapters of the *Commodity Trading Manual*. After you've read Chapters 1-7, review the highlights below, then try your hand at answering the questions at the end of the section. If you have a problem answering any of them, be sure to reread the related material in the *CTM*.

**Chapter 1
Development
of the
Marketplace**

♦ Today's futures markets and the principles that underlie commodity futures trading evolved from practices that are centuries old.

♦ Commodity markets in the United States existed as early as 1752 and traded domestic produce, textiles, hides, metals, and lumber. Most transactions were cash transactions for immediate delivery.

♦ The history of modern futures trading was tied closely to the development of commerce in Chicago and the grain trade in the Midwest. Chicago's strategic location at the base of the Great Lakes, close to the fertile farmlands of the Midwest, contributed to the city's rapid growth and development as a grain terminal. Problems of supply and demand, transportation, and storage, however, led to a chaotic marketing situation and the logical development of futures markets.

♦ As grain trade expanded in the Midwest, a centralized marketplace— the Chicago Board of Trade—was formed in 1848. Its purpose was to promote the commerce of the city and to provide a place where buyers and sellers could meet to exchange commodities. During the exchange's early years, forward contracts were used.

♦ A forward contract is an agreement in which a seller agrees to deliver a specific cash commodity to a buyer sometime in the future. Forward contracts had their drawbacks, i.e., they were not standardized, and traders often did not fulfill these forward commitments.

♦ During the late 1800s, the Chicago Board of Trade formalized grain trading by establishing formal trading practices, setting up new clearing and settlement procedures, and developing standardized agreements called *futures contracts*.

♦ Futures contracts, in contrast to forward contracts, are standardized as to quality, quantity, and time and place of delivery for the commodity being traded.

♦ The first financial futures contracts began trading in the 1970s.

♦ Options on futures were instituted in 1982. In contrast to futures, options allow investors and risk managers to define and limit risk in the form of a premium paid for the right to buy or sell a futures contract. Options also provide the buyer with unlimited profit potential.

♦ Options on Treasury bond futures began trading in October 1982 at the Chicago Board of Trade as part of a government pilot program. The success of this contract opened the way for options on agricultural and other financial futures.

♦ The futures industry is becoming more international in scope each year, with U.S. exchanges expanding their markets to foreign investors and more and more futures exchanges opening overseas.

♦ Two primary purposes of the futures markets are price-risk transfer and price discovery.

♦ A cash market is a place where people buy and sell actual commodities, e.g., a grain elevator, a bank, etc.

♦ Futures markets are trading arenas where buyers and sellers trade futures contracts—standardized, legal agreements to make or take delivery of a specific commodity at a designated place sometime in the future. The only variable is price, which is discovered through an auctionlike process on the trading floor of an organized futures exchange.

♦ Cash contracts are sales agreements for either the immediate or future delivery of a commodity. One type of cash contract is a forward contract.

♦ Because futures contracts are standardized, sellers and buyers are able to exchange one contract for another and actually offset their obligation to deliver or take delivery of the cash commodity underlying the futures contract. Offset in the futures market means taking another futures position opposite and equal to one's initial futures transaction.

♦ Hedging, a major economic purpose of futures markets, is the buying and selling of futures contracts to offset the risks of changing prices in the cash markets. This risk-transfer mechanism has made futures contracts virtually indispensable in efforts to control costs and protect profit margins.

♦ Speculators assume the risk hedgers try to avoid. While profit is the motive of speculators, they make it possible for hedgers to offset their price risk. This is because speculators provide vital risk-shifting opportunities to hedgers, adding liquidity and capital to the markets.

♦ Essential to the marketplace are clearinghouses, which are responsible for settling trading accounts, clearing trades, collecting and maintaining

**Chapter 2
Overview
of Futures
Trading**

margin monies, regulating delivery of clearing member firms, and reporting trade data.

♦ The price of a product is discovered by changes in its supply and demand. Supply is the quantity of a product that sellers are willing to provide to the market at a given price. Demand is the quantity of a product buyers are willing to purchase from the market at a given price.

♦ Futures prices are the most widely used pricing reference in domestic and international financial, metal, and agricultural markets. Once prices are discovered, the futures exchanges are responsible for disseminating these prices to the public on a daily basis through market reporting systems and newspapers.

Chapter 3
U.S. Futures Exchanges

♦ Most U.S. futures exchanges are not-for-profit membership associations incorporated in the states in which they are located.

♦ Membership in each exchange is limited to a specific number of individuals, although some exchanges permit members to hold multiple memberships.

♦ An exchange conducts a thorough investigation of each member applicant.

♦ Special memberships or trading privileges have been offered by some exchanges.

♦ The government of each exchange is vested in a board and its officers.

♦ Committees, composed of exchange members, advise and assist the board and perform specific duties related to exchange operations.

♦ An administrative staff carries out the policies and decisions of the board and the committees.

Chapter 4
Exchange Floor Operations

♦ Futures exchanges provide a location for buyers and sellers to meet and, through an open outcry auction process, discover a price for specific futures and options contracts. Exchanges also are responsible for disseminating these prices and guaranteeing fulfillment of traded contracts. This activity is centralized on an exchange's trading floor.

♦ All market participants have indirect access to the floor through their brokers; however, only exchange members have the privilege of trading on the floor.

♦ Men and women who trade on the floor perform a variety of functions. Brokers fill outside orders. Others trade hedging or speculative accounts for the company they work for. Locals, a third group, trade for their own account and speculate on future price movements.

♦ Local traders can use a variety of trading techniques. They can establish day trades, i.e., initiate and offset a position during one day's trading session. Locals can initiate position trades, i.e., hold long or short positions over a period of days or weeks. Locals also may trade for small, short-term profits during the course of each trading session, rarely carrying a position overnight. This type of trading is known as *scalping*.

♦ Offers to buy or sell are made by shouting out prices in an auction style so that each trader in the pit has an opportunity to take the opposite side of a trade.

♦ An important verbal distinction shows if a trader wants to buy or sell. Buyers call out (bid) price first and then quantity; sellers call out (offer) quantity first, then price.

♦ Futures exchanges are free markets where the many factors that influence supply and demand converge on the trading floor and through open outcry auction are translated into a single figure—a price.

♦ Because the same economic forces that influence cash prices also affect futures prices, futures prices closely parallel the actual cash values of commodities and financial instruments.

♦ Millions of people all over the world use the price information generated by futures markets.

♦ Transactions made on the trading floor must be reported to the membership and the general public. This is accomplished by futures exchanges through a variety of communications systems. These include specialized computer systems that transmit price information as prices are discovered. Newspapers also carry this information on a daily basis.

♦ A Futures Commission Merchant (FCM) is an individual or firm that transacts futures and options business on behalf of financial and commercial institutions as well as the general public.

♦ There are a number of terms used to describe FCMs, including *wire houses*, *brokerage houses*, and *commission houses*.

♦ The basic function of an FCM is to represent the interests of those in the market who do not hold a seat on a futures exchange.

Chapter 5
The Customer and the Futures Commission Merchant

♦ Services provided by FCMs include: placing orders, collecting and segregating margin monies, providing basic accounting records, disseminating market information and research, and counseling and training customers in futures and options trading practices and strategies.

♦ Most customer operations are handled by Associated Persons (APs), who are employed or associated with an FCM, an Introducing Broker (IB), Commodity Trading Advisor (CTA), or Commodity Pool Operator (CPO). All of these individuals or organizations must be registered with the Commodity Futures Trading Commission (CFTC), through the National Futures Association (NFA), and become NFA members.

♦ Exchange members who act as floor brokers must register with the CFTC. Registration is not required of exchange members who trade solely for their own accounts.

♦ Everyone other than exchange members who handles customer accounts must pass the National Commodity Futures Exam (Series 3), administered by the National Association of Securities Dealers, and register with the CFTC.

♦ There are different types of accounts a customer can open with a broker, including an individual account, a joint account, or a discretionary account. In individual accounts, trading decisions are made by the individual. In joint accounts, all parties have input on trading decisions. Either type of account may be opened for hedging or speculating purposes. In a discretionary account (also known as a *controlled* or *managed account*), the customer authorizes another person to make all trading decisions. Each exchange and FCM has specific rules for handling discretionary accounts. One of the most essential is the customer's written power of attorney to exercise discretion. The only way to terminate the trading authority established in a discretionary account is by written revocation of the power of attorney either on the part of the customer or the person controlling the account.

♦ Performance bond margins must be posted by all futures market participants. They are financial guarantees required of both buyers and sellers to ensure fulfillment of the futures contract.

♦ Futures margins are determined on the basis of risk. In a volatile (or risky) market, a higher margin is usually required; and in a less volatile (or less risky) market, a lower margin is usually required.

♦ Margin levels also vary for hedging and speculating accounts. For example, exchanges and brokerage firms generally require lower margins for hedging accounts because they carry less risk than speculating accounts.

♦ Initial margin is the amount a market participant must deposit into his margin account at the time he places an order to buy or sell a futures contract. Then, on a daily basis, a brokerage firm debits and credits each customer's margin account based on the close of that day's trading session. This debiting and crediting is referred to as *marking-to-the-market.*

♦ A customer must maintain a set minimum margin known as maintenance margin (per outstanding futures contract) in his account. On any day that debits resulting from a market loss reduce the funds in the account below the maintenance margin, the broker calls on his customer for an additional deposit to restore the account to the initial margin level. Requests for additional money are known as *margin calls.*

♦ There are a variety of trading orders used in the futures markets, including: market, price limit, fill-or-kill, stop, stop-limit, market-if-touched, time limit, opening, closing, cancellation, and combination orders.

♦ A market order states the number of contracts of a given delivery month a customer wants to buy or sell. The order is executed as soon as possible at the best possible price.

♦ A price limit order specifies the price limit at which the customer's order must be executed. It can be executed only at that price or better. One type of price limit order is a fill-or-kill order. It must be filled immediately or be canceled.

♦ Stop orders are normally used to liquidate earlier transactions, to cut losses, or to protect profits. A stop order is not executed until the market reaches a given price level. A stop order to buy becomes a market order when the futures contract trades (or is bid) at or above the stop price. A stop order to sell becomes a market order when the futures contract trades (or is offered) at or below the stop price. A variation of the stop order is the stop-limit order. With a stop-limit order, the trade must be executed at the exact price or held until the stated price is reached again.

♦ A market-if-touched order may be executed only if the market reaches a particular price.

♦ A time limit order is good until a designated time during the trading session. If the order has not been filled by that time, it is automatically canceled.

♦ A cancel order deletes a customer's previous order.

♦ Combination orders are used to enter two orders at the same time. One-cancels-other and spread orders are examples of combination orders.

Chapter 6
Clearing
Operations

♦ Clearinghouses of U.S. commodity exchanges, such as the Board of Trade Clearing Corporation, are responsible for settling accounts, clearing trades, collecting and maintaining margin monies, and regulating delivery of all clearing member firms.

♦ Only members of an exchange's clearinghouse can clear a trade made on the floor of a futures exchange. Memberships in clearing organizations are usually held by companies.

♦ If a firm is not a member of the clearinghouse, it must clear its trades through a clearing member firm.

♦ Financial requirements to become a member of a clearinghouse are rigid to help ensure the financial soundness of the clearinghouses.

♦ Clearinghouses act as third parties to all futures and options contracts—acting as a buyer to every clearing member seller and a seller to every clearing member buyer. Buyers and sellers of futures and options contracts do not create financial obligations to one another, but, rather, to the clearinghouse through their clearing member firms.

♦ Clearinghouses are able to guarantee all trades made on the floor of exchanges because they require members to deposit margin monies based upon their customers' positions. Clearing margins act as financial safeguards to ensure that clearing member firms perform on their customers' open futures and options contracts.

♦ Clearing margins are distinct from brokerage (customer) margins, which individual buyers and sellers of futures and options contracts are required to deposit with their brokers.

♦ Initial clearing margin is the amount a clearing member firm must have on account at the time an order is placed to buy or sell a futures contract.

♦ As a clearing member's position changes from day to day, so does the required margin. After each trading session, the clearinghouse recomputes the margin requirement for each clearing member. Every evening, the clearinghouse provides a margin statement to the clearing firm. If a net position increases, additional margin must be deposited before the market opens the next day.

♦ In most cases, initial margins are sufficient to cover daily maximum price fluctuations. At the Chicago Board of Trade, initial margin deposits are collected within 24 hours of the time a trade is executed (in some instances, within 10 hours).

♦ In periods of great market volatility or in the case of high-risk accounts, the clearinghouse can call on a clearing member firm to deposit additional margin money at anytime during a trading session to cover adverse price changes. This call for additional money is known as a *variation margin call*, and, within one hour, the member firm must pay the amount called for by wire transfer of funds. This amount is applied to the settlement for the day and does not go into the standing or initial margin account.

♦ Every day, the clearinghouse settles the accounts of its clearing member firms and adjusts each one based on that day's market gains or losses. This debiting and crediting on the basis of price changes is called *marking-to-the-market*. Accounts are adjusted by calculating the difference between the day's settlement price and the price at which the position was initiated. In the case of options on futures, the full premium is received from the buyer and passed on to the seller.

♦ Although the method of determining the settlement price varies among exchanges, the following methods are the most common. When there is a single price at the close of trading, that price becomes the settlement price. However, in the flurry of last-minute trading, it is common for several separate transactions to be made at different but closely related prices. In this circumstance, averaging the closing range is the most common way to determine the settlement price.

♦ All open futures positions are liquidated by either offset or delivery. The vast majority are settled by offsetting trades; yet buyers and sellers can take or make delivery of the commodity or financial instrument.

♦ Clearinghouses generally provide the mechanics that enable sellers to make delivery to qualified buyers. The delivery process varies from exchange to exchange but, in all cases, delivery is possible by completing a series of steps.

♦ Daily recording of trading volume and open interest is a service provided by all clearing organizations. Trading volume is the number of contracts traded of each delivery month of every futures and options contract. Open interest is the total number of futures and options contracts of a given commodity that have not yet been offset by an opposite futures or options transaction nor fulfilled by delivery of the commodity or option exercise. Each open transaction has a buyer and a seller; but for calculation of open interest, only one side of the contract is counted.

♦ U.S. futures markets have a long history of self-regulation that dates from the mid-1800s.

♦ Exchange rules and regulations cover many areas of futures trading— from contract specifications to trading practices.

**Chapter 7
Regulation
of Futures
Trading**

♦ Trading rules and regulations are scrutinized continuously by exchanges, and are periodically amended to reflect the needs of market users. The adoption of many new rules and regulations, as well as the amendment of existing ones, requires the approval of the Commodity Futures Trading Commission (CFTC), the U.S. federal regulatory agency for futures and options on futures trading.

♦ U.S. futures exchanges are required by state and federal laws to regulate the conduct of exchange members, member firms, and their employees. The obligation of the exchanges to enforce their own rules and regulations was enhanced in the 1900s with the passing of several federal acts, including the Grain Futures Act of 1922, the Commodity Exchange Act of 1936, the Commodity Futures Trading Commission Act of 1974, and the Futures Trading Acts of 1978, 1982, and 1986.

♦ Under the Grain Futures Act of 1922, futures trading in specific commodities could take place only on federally licensed exchanges.

♦ The Commodity Exchange Act of 1936 created the Commodity Exchange Commission, which was responsible for a variety of duties, including: licensing futures exchanges, determining procedures for registering FCMs and floor brokers, and enforcing the Commodity Exchange Act.

♦ The CFTC Act of 1974 created an independent federal regulatory agency for futures and options on futures trading, i.e., the Commodity Futures Trading Commission, to replace the Commodity Exchange Authority of the U.S. Department of Agriculture.

♦ The CFTC's regulatory powers extend to exchange actions and to the review and approval of futures and options contracts proposed by a futures exchange.

♦ The National Futures Association (NFA) was created under the CFTC Act of 1974. The NFA is an industrywide, industry-supported, self-regulatory organization for the futures industry.

♦ Primary responsibilities of the NFA are to: (1) enforce ethical standards and customer protection rules, (2) screen futures professionals for membership, (3) audit and monitor futures professionals for financial and general compliance rules, (4) provide for arbitration of futures-related disputes, and (5) promote consumer and member education concerning the NFA's role in the futures industry.

Take the time to test your futures and options knowledge by answering the following questions. After taking the test, score yourself by referring to the answers at the end of the section. If you have more than four errors, review the material in Section One and Chapters 1-7 of the *Commodity Trading Manual* before going on.

Fill-In
Using the list of words below, complete the following sentences.

cash contract
cash market
CFTC
Chicago Board of Trade
clearinghouse
delivery
demand
discretionary account
equilibrium price
Futures Commission Merchant
futures contract
futures exchanges
futures prices
hedging
individual account

joint account
margin
marking-to-the-market
National Commodity Futures
    Exam (Series 3)
National Futures Association
offset
open interest
open outcry
price discovery
risk transfer
speculating
supply
trading volume

1. A(n) _____ transacts futures and/or options on futures business on behalf of financial and commercial institutions as well as the general public.

2. Debiting and crediting a margin account, on a daily basis, for either a customer or a clearing member account is referred to as _____.

3. Created under the CFTC Act of 1974, the _____ is an industrywide, industry-supported, self-regulatory organization for the futures industry.

4. A(n) _____ acts as a buyer to every clearing member seller and a seller to every clearing member buyer.

5. _____ is buying and selling futures and/or options on futures contracts to offset price risk in the cash market.

6. The price of a product is discovered by changes in its _____ and _____.

7. Two primary purposes of the futures market are _____ and _____.

8. All futures positions can be liquidated by _____ or
   _____.

9. Most _____ are not-for-profit membership
   associations.

10. In a(n) _____ the customer authorizes another
    person to make all trading decisions.

11. _____ are the most widely used pricing reference in
    domestic and international financial, metal, and agricultural
    markets.

Multiple Choice
Select the best answer for the following questions.

12. Speculators are necessary to the futures market because they:
    A. Add to market liquidity
    B. Aid in the price discovery process
    C. Make it possible for hedgers to offset price risk
    D. All of the above

13. The federal regulatory agency that oversees futures and options on
    futures trading is the:
    A. Commodity Exchange Authority
    B. Commodity Futures Trading Commission
    C. National Futures Association
    D. Futures Industry Association

14. A cash forward contract is:
    A. Standardized
    B. An agreement to buy or sell a cash commodity
    C. One type of a futures contract
    D. Traded on all futures exchanges

15. Today's futures markets:
    A. Are becoming more international in scope
    B. Trade options on securities such as stocks
    C. Are the same as cash markets, since they allow delivery of the
       cash commodity
    D. All of the above

Answers

1. **Futures Commission Merchant.** FCMs represent the interests of those who do not hold a seat on a futures exchange. Some of the services they provide include: placing orders, collecting and segregating margin monies, providing basic accounting records, disseminating market information and research, and counseling and training customers in trading practices.

2. **Marking-to-the-market.** Each margin account (regardless of whether it's a customer account at a brokerage firm or a clearing member account at a clearinghouse) is debited or credited, on a daily basis, based on the settlement price of that day's trading session. This system protects buyers and sellers against contract default.

3. **National Futures Association.** Established in 1981, the NFA is responsible for enforcing customer protection rules; screening new members; providing a system for arbitration; and promoting consumer/member education.

4. **Clearinghouse.** Buyers and sellers of futures and options contracts do not create financial obligations to one another, but, rather, to the clearinghouse through their clearing member firms.

5. **Hedging.** A major economic purpose of futures markets is hedging. This risk-transfer mechanism has made futures contracts and options on futures virtually indispensable in efforts to control costs and protect profit margins.

6. **Supply, demand.** The price of a product or commodity depends on the relationship between its supply and demand.

7. **Price discovery, risk transfer.** Futures markets make it possible for hedgers to transfer price risk to those who are willing to accept it— speculators. Futures markets also provide price information that the world looks to as a benchmark in determining the value of a particular commodity or financial instrument.

8. **Offset, delivery.** All open futures positions are either offset or delivered against the contract. The vast majority are settled by offsetting trades, and only 1 to 3 percent result in delivery of the actual commodity.

9. **Futures exchanges.** Most exchanges are not-for-profit associations incorporated in the states in which they are located. Membership in each exchange is limited to a specific number of individuals, although some exchanges permit the holding of multiple memberships.

10. **Discretionary account.** Also known as a *controlled* or *managed account*, a discretionary account can be set up in which the customer authorizes another person to make all trading decisions.

11. **Futures prices.** Once prices are discovered, the exchanges are responsible for disseminating this information to the public.

12. **D.** Speculators perform all three functions.

13. **B.** The CFTC regulatory powers extend to exchange actions and to the review and approval of futures contracts proposed by an exchange.

14. **B.** Cash forward contracts are agreements between buyers and sellers to purchase a cash commodity to be delivered sometime in the future. Unlike futures contracts, cash forward contracts are not standardized.

15. **A.** The futures industry, sensitive to the marketplace and its function as a risk-management mechanism, has become more international in scope. Futures exchanges trade options on futures—not options on securities. While market participants can make or take delivery of a cash commodity to offset their futures position, futures markets trade futures contracts—not cash contracts.

SECTION TWO—HEDGING

The following highlights cover topics presented in Chapter 8 of the *Commodity Trading Manual*. After you've read Chapter 8, review the highlights below, then try your hand at answering the questions at the end of the section. If you have a problem answering any of them, be sure to reread the material in the CTM.

♦ A primary economic function of futures markets is price-risk management, the most common method of which is hedging.

♦ Hedging, in its simplest form, is the practice of offsetting the price risk inherent in any cash market position by taking an equal but opposite position in the futures market.

♦ Hedgers are individuals or companies that own or are planning to own a cash commodity—corn, soybeans, wheat, U.S. Treasury bonds, notes, bills, etc.—and are concerned that the cost of the commodity may change before they either buy or sell it.

♦ To an experienced hedger, it is more important to establish a market objective that protects his investment than worry about the possibility of a missed profit opportunity.

Cash/Futures Relationship: Basis

♦ Cash market transactions involve the purchase and sale of actual physical commodities at current prices.

♦ Futures market transactions involve the purchase and sale of futures contracts, which are standardized agreements to take or make delivery of a specific commodity at a predetermined place and time in the future.

♦ The difference between the cash price of a commodity at a specific location and the price of a specific futures contract for the same commodity is defined as the basis. To calculate basis, subtract the futures price from the cash price. Basis = cash price – futures price

♦ To calculate the basis in T-bond or T-note futures contracts, the futures price is adjusted to a futures-cash equivalent. The change to a cash equivalent is made using a conversion factor to compare the cash market price of a T-bond or note with the 8 percent coupon standard of the T-bond or T-note futures contract. The conversion factor is multiplied by the futures price to obtain a cash equivalent. Basis = (bond or note cash price) – (futures price × bond or note conversion factor)

♦ The basis can be either positive or negative, depending upon whether the cash price is higher or lower than the futures price. If the basis moves from 10 to 1, it has become more negative (less positive). On the other hand, if the basis moves from –5 to 2, the basis has become more positive (less negative). If the cash and futures prices are the same, the basis is expressed as zero.

♦ By knowing the basis, the hedger can replace the risk of price fluctuation with the lesser risk of a change in the relationship between the cash and the futures price of the commodity.

♦ The costs of storing grain—known as *carrying charges*—normally are reflected in grain and oilseed futures prices for different delivery months. Because of this, the price of the nearby futures contract is normally lower than the price of the deferred contract month. Carrying charges include not only the cost of using the storage facilities, but also such costs as insurance on the harvested crop and interest on the invested capital.

Carrying Charges

♦ An *inverted market* refers to a futures market in which the relationship between two delivery months of the same commodity is abnormal.

♦ With interest rate futures contracts, the cost of carry reflects the actual costs of financing an investment. It includes any interest payments received, less any short-term borrowing costs, initial margin deposit, variation margin requirements, if any, and transaction costs.

Cost of Carry

♦ Cost of carry can be either positive or negative. If it is positive, it can be profitable to hold a financial instrument until delivery. Under this "normal" market environment, the cash instrument is priced at a premium to the futures contract. Since these gains increase as the holding period increases, the nearby futures contract trades at a premium to the deferred.

♦ If the cost of carry is negative, the investor loses money holding the investment until delivery. To compensate for a negative carry, the cash instrument trades at a discount to the futures contract. Since carrying costs rise as the holding period increases, the futures price of the nearby contract month trades at a discount to the deferred contract month.

♦ Cost of carry is reflected in the yield curve. A positive yield curve exists when long-term interest rates are higher than short-term interest rates. A negative yield curve exists when short-term interest rates are higher than long-term interest rates.

♦ When interest rates rise, the prices of interest rate futures and cash market instruments decline; when interest rates decline, prices of interest rate futures and cash market instruments rise.

♦ The fundamental reason why hedging works is that futures and cash prices of a related commodity tend to respond to the same economic factors. And, as a futures contract nears expiration, cash and futures prices tend to converge. Delivery, arbitrage, and exchange for physicals are some of the economic factors that allow this to occur.

Hedging: A Two-Step Process

♦ Hedging is a two-step process. Depending upon the hedger's cash market situation, he will either buy or sell futures as his first position. His next step will be to offset his opening position before the futures contract expires by taking a second position opposite the opening transaction.

♦ If a hedger's first position involves the sale of futures contracts, it is referred to as a *selling*, or *short*, hedge. The purpose of a short hedge is to lock in a selling price.

♦ If a hedger's first position involves the purchase of futures contracts, it is referred to as a *buying*, or *long*, hedge. The purpose of a long hedge is to lock in a buying price.

♦ To compensate for the greater decline in the dollar value of a cash bond versus the decline in the futures price, a weighted hedge is used.

Self-Test

Take the time to test your hedging knowledge by answering the following questions. After taking the test, score yourself by referring to the answers at the end of the section. If you have more than four errors, review the material in Section Two and Chapter 8 of the *Commodity Trading Manual* before going on.

Fill-In
Using the list of words below, complete the following sentences.

arbitrage	delivery
basis	exchange for physicals (EFP)
buying (long) hedge	hedging
carrying charges	interest rates
cheapest to deliver	rise
converge	selling (short) hedge
conversion factor	weighted hedge
decline	yield curve

1. To protect the price he'll receive for his soybeans at harvesttime, a farmer will initiate a(n) _____ in the spring.

2. _____ is the difference between the cash price of a commodity and the price of a specific futures contract for the same commodity.

3. A(n) _____ is used to compensate for the greater decline in the dollar value of a cash bond versus the decline in the futures price.

4. As a futures contract nears expiration, the cash and futures prices of the same commodity tend to _____.

5. A(n) _____ is used to compare the cash market price of T-bonds or T-notes with the price of a specific futures contract for the same instrument.

6. The costs of storing grains are known as _____.

7. When interest rates rise, the prices of interest rate futures and cash market instruments _____; when interest rates fall, the prices of interest rate futures and cash market instruments

   _____.

8. A portfolio manager expects interest rates to fall over the next six months. To protect his anticipated Treasury bond purchase price, he initiates a _____.

9. _____ is the act of taking a futures position opposite one's cash position.

10. The relationship between long-term and short-term interest rates is reflected in the _____.

Problems

11. Assume a flour miller plans to buy 10,000 bushels of wheat in April to meet his operating needs, but he's concerned that prices may rise between now (November 1) and April. To protect himself, he establishes a hedge using CBOT May wheat futures. (One CBOT wheat futures contract equals 5,000 bushels.) At the time, cash wheat is selling for $3.45/bushel and CBOT May wheat futures are trading at $3.60/bushel.

   On April 15, the miller purchases wheat locally at $3.65/bushel and offsets his futures position at $3.95/bushel.

   A. To protect himself in case wheat prices rise before he actually purchases the cash wheat, the flour miller would establish a hedge by:

     1. Buying 2 May wheat futures
     2. Selling 2 May wheat futures
     3. Buying 4 May wheat futures
     4. Selling 4 May wheat futures

B. Is this a short or long hedge?

C. Complete the following T-account:

Cash	Futures
Nov 1	
Apr 15	

Result
Cash purchase price
Futures gain or loss
Net purchase price

12. On December 1, a portfolio manager holds $500,000 of 8 percent U.S. T-bonds currently priced at 93-00. He intends to sell the Treasury portfolio in the next few months. However, he is concerned that interest rates will increase in the interim, thus lowering the portfolio's value. He decides to hedge his 8 percent bonds using the CBOT March T-bond futures contract, which is currently priced at 92-24. (One CBOT T-bond futures contract equals $100,000 face value U.S. Treasury bonds.)

    By February 15, interest rates have increased. The value of the manager's 8 percent bonds has decreased to 91-00, and the March T-bond contract has dropped to 90-28. He sells his 8 percent bonds and offsets his position in the CBOT March T-bond futures contract.

A. Basing his hedge solely on the face value of his portfolio versus that of the futures contract, the manager would:
     1. Buy 5 Mar T-bond futures
     2. Sell 5 Mar T-bond futures
     3. Buy 8 Mar T-bond futures
     4. Sell 8 Mar T-bond futures

B. Is this a long or short hedge?

C. Complete the following T-account:

Cash	Futures
Dec 1	
Feb 15	
Result	

Result
Cash sale price
Futures gain or loss
Net sale price

13. Assume in June a film manufacturer estimates he'll need to purchase 25,000 troy ounces of silver in December for his manufacturing needs. He expects prices to rise between now and the time he actually plans to purchase the silver in the cash market but would like to take advantage of today's price of $5.60/ounce. So, on June 15 he establishes a hedge. At the time, CBOT's December silver futures are trading at $5.90/ounce. (One CBOT silver futures contract equals 1,000 troy ounces.)

On November 19, silver is selling for $8/ounce in the cash market and the December futures contract is trading at $8.45/ounce.

A. Would the film manufacturer establish a short or long hedge?

B. Complete the T-account on the next page to show the film manufacturer's first and second steps to hedge the purchase price for silver.

Cash	Futures
Jun 15	
Nov 19	

Result
Cash purchase price
Futures gain or loss
Net purchase price

For Further Practice

14. A portfolio manager is told on July 1 to expect a cash inflow of $300,000 on August 15. She would like to invest that money in 8 percent five-year U.S. Treasury notes at their current price of 98-16, and worries that prices will increase before the money becomes available. To hedge against an increase in the price of five-year T-notes to be bought on August 15, she decides to use the September five-year T-note futures contract, which is currently priced at 98-10. (One CBOT T-note futures contract equals $100,000 face value U.S. Treasury notes.)

By August 15, interest rates have fallen and the price of the September five-year T-note futures contract has consequently increased to 99-14. The manager offsets her position in the September five-year T-note futures contract, and buys 8 percent five-year U.S. T-notes at their current price of 99-16.

A. Basing her hedge solely on the face value of the five-year T-notes to be purchased versus that of the futures contract, the manager would:
   1. Sell 8 Sep five-year T-note futures
   2. Sell 3 Sep five-year T-note futures
   3. Buy 8 Sep five-year T-note futures
   4. Buy 3 Sep five-year T-note futures

B. Is this a long or short hedge?

C. Complete the T-account below to show the portfolio manager's first and second steps to hedge against a possible price increase in five-year T-notes.

Cash	Futures
Jul 1	
Aug 15	

Result
Cash purchase price
Futures gain or loss
Net purchase price

15. An Illinois farmer expects to harvest at least 20,000 bushels of soybeans in September. He has no on-farm storage and wants to establish a selling price for his cash beans in the spring because he's concerned that prices will fall. Assume that on May 15 he establishes a hedge. At the time, CBOT November soybean futures are trading at $6.10 and the cash forward bid for delivery at harvest is $5.88. (One CBOT soybean futures contract equals 5,000 bushels.)

On October 1, when the farmer delivers 20,000 bushels of soybeans to the local elevator, he offsets the hedge. November futures are trading at $5.70 and the cash price is $5.51. Based on this information, answer the following questions:

A. To hedge himself against a possible drop in market prices, the farmer would:
   1. Buy 4 Nov soybean futures
   2. Sell 4 Nov soybean futures
   3. Buy 2 Nov soybean futures
   4. Sell 2 Nov soybean futures

B. Is this a long or short hedge?

C. Complete the T-account on the next page to show the farmer's first and second steps to hedge against a possible price decrease in soybean prices.

Cash	Futures	Basis
May 15		
Oct 1		

Result
Cash sale price
Futures gain or loss
Net sale price

D. What was the basis (1) in May? _____ (2) at delivery? _____

E. How was the actual selling price affected by the change in the basis?

1. **Selling hedge.** The primary purpose of a short hedge is to establish a fixed selling price.

2. **Basis.** The basis cannot be predicted precisely, but it is generally less volatile than either the futures or cash price. By knowing the basis, the hedger can replace the risk of price fluctuation with the lesser risk of a change in the relationship between cash and futures prices.

3. **Weighted hedge.** In a weighted hedge, a market participant adjusts the number of T-bond or T-note futures contracts to effectively hedge a bond or note cash position. One way to determine the number of futures contracts needed is to multiply the conversion factor of the debt instrument by the par value of cash bonds divided by the par value of the futures contract. Number of futures contracts = conversion factor × (par value of cash bond/par value of futures contract)

4. **Converge.** The fundamental reason why hedging works is that futures and cash prices of a related commodity tend to respond to the same economic factors. And, as a futures contract nears expiration, cash and futures prices tend to converge; that is, the basis approaches zero.

5. **Conversion factor.** The futures price of a specific T-bond or T-note is multiplied by a conversion factor to obtain the futures-cash equivalent.

6. **Carrying charges.** The cost of using storage facilities, insurance costs, and interest on the invested capital are included in carrying charges.

7. **Decline, rise.** An inverse relationship exists between interest rates and the prices of interest rate futures and cash market instruments.

8. **Buying hedge.** The purpose of a long hedge is to establish a fixed purchase price. With financial instruments, the long hedge not only establishes a purchase price, it locks in a yield.

9. **Hedging.** Hedging is the practice of offsetting the price risk inherent in any cash market position by taking an equal but opposite position in the futures market. Hedgers use the futures markets to protect their businesses from adverse price changes.

10. **Yield curve.** The yield curve is a chart visually depicting the current yield for all debt instruments with the same rating over an extended time period.

11. A. **1.** To protect the purchase price for wheat, he would take a position in the futures market opposite his cash position. Since he's currently short wheat, the miller would buy futures to establish a long futures position. Two contracts would be purchased, since one CBOT wheat contract equals 5,000 bushels (2 × 5,000 = 10,000).

   B. **Long hedge.** A long hedge is established to protect his purchase price.

   C.

Cash	Futures
Nov 1	
Needs 10,000 bu of wheat in Apr; wheat is at $3.45/bu	Buys 2 May wheat contracts at $3.60/bu
Apr 15	
Acquires 10,000 bu of wheat at $3.65/bu	Sells 2 May wheat contracts at $3.95/bu
Result	
Cash purchase price	$3.65/bu
Futures gain	–0.35/bu
Net purchase price	$3.30/bu

12. A. **2.** To protect the selling price for T-bonds, he would take a position in the futures market opposite his cash position. Since he's currently long bonds, the portfolio manager would sell futures to establish a short futures position. Five contracts would be sold, since one CBOT T-bond contract equals $100,000 face value U.S. T-bonds (5 × 100,000 = 500,000).

   B. **Short hedge.** A short hedge is used to protect the selling price of a commodity.

C.

Cash	Futures
Dec 1	
Holds T-bonds at 93-00, or $465,000 total for $500,000 par value	Sells 5 Mar T-bond contracts at 92-24, or $463,750 total
Feb 15	
Sells T-bonds at 91-00, or $455,000	Buys 5 Mar T-bond contracts at 90-28, or $454,375
Result	
Cash sale price	$455,000
Futures gain	+9,375
Net sale price	$464,375

13. A. **Long hedge.** To protect the purchase price for silver, the film manufacturer would take a position in the futures market opposite his cash position. Since he's currently short silver, he would buy futures to establish a long hedge. Twenty-five contracts would be purchased, since one CBOT silver contract equals 1,000 troy ounces (25 × 1,000 = 25,000).

B.

Cash	Futures
Jun 15	
Needs 25,000 oz of silver in Dec; silver at $5.60/oz	Buys 25 Dec silver contracts at $5.90/oz
Nov 19	
Acquires 25,000 oz of silver at $8.00/oz	Closes long position by selling 25 Dec silver contracts at $8.45/oz
Result	
Cash purchase price	$8.00/troy oz
Futures gain	−2.55/troy oz
Net purchase price	$5.45/troy oz

14. A. **4.** The portfolio manager would buy T-note futures to protect the purchase price. Three contracts would be purchased, since one five-year T-note contract equals $100,000 par value of U.S. T-notes (3 × 100,000 = 300,000).

B. **Long hedge.** A long hedge is initiated to protect the price the manager will have to pay for T-notes in the cash market.

C.

Cash	Futures
Jul 1	
Plans to invest $300,000 in T-notes; T-notes at 98-16, or $295,500 for $300,000 par value	Buys 3 Sep T-note contracts at 98-10, or $294,937.50 total
Aug 15	
Buys T-notes at 99-16, or $298,500 total	Sells 3 Sep T-note contracts at 99-14, or $298,312.50 total
Result	
Cash purchase price	$298,500
Futures gain	–3,375
Net purchase price	$295,125

15. A. **2.** The farmer would sell four soybean contracts to protect his selling price. One CBOT soybean futures contract equals 5,000 bushels.

B. **Short hedge.** A short hedge is initiated to protect the selling price.

C.

Cash	Futures	Basis
May 15		
Plans to harvest 20,000 bu of soybeans in Sep; soybeans at $5.88/bu	Sells 4 Nov soybean contracts at $6.10	$–.22
Oct 1		
Sells 20,000 bu of soybeans locally at $5.51/bu	Buys 4 Nov soybean contracts at $5.70/bu	$–.19
Result		
Cash sale price	$5.51/bu	
Futures gain	+0.40/bu	
Net sale price	$5.91/bu	

D. (1) **22 cents under November futures;** (2) **19 cents under November futures**

E. Because the basis became less negative, moving from 22 cents under November futures to 19 cents under November futures, the **actual cash selling price increased.**

SECTION THREE—SPECULATING

The following highlights cover topics presented in Chapter 9 of the *Commodity Trading Manual*. After you've read the chapter, review the highlights below, then try your hand at answering the questions at the end of the section. If you have a problem answering any of them, be sure to reread the material in the *CTM*.

♦ Speculators are market participants who try to profit from buying and selling futures and/or options contracts by anticipating future price movements.

♦ Speculators assume price risk—risk that already exists for producers and users of commodities or financial instruments. Speculators provide hedgers with vital risk-shifting opportunities, which add liquidity and capital to the futures markets.

Speculators Add Liquidity and Capital to the Markets

♦ In addition to assuming risk and providing liquidity and capital, speculators help to ensure the stability of the market.

♦ Unlike hedgers, speculators rarely have an interest in owning the cash commodity or financial instrument that underlies a futures contract. They buy contracts when expecting prices to increase, hoping to later make an offsetting sale at a higher price and, thus, a profit. They sell contracts when expecting prices to fall, hoping to later make an offsetting purchase at a lower price and, again, a profit.

Types of Speculators

♦ If a speculator is long futures, then he has purchased one or more futures contracts; if a speculator is short futures, then he has sold one or more futures contracts.

♦ Speculators' futures and options positions must be reported periodically to the CFTC after they reach a specific number of open contracts. These speculators are classified as large position holders.

♦ One method of categorizing speculators is by the price-forecasting methods they use. Fundamental analysts look at supply and demand factors; technical analysts use charts to plot price, volume, and open interest movements in current and recent years.

♦ Position traders initiate a futures or options position and then hold it over a period of days, weeks, or months.

♦ Day traders hold market positions only during the course of a trading session and rarely carry a position overnight.

♦ Scalpers are professional traders who trade for themselves in the pits. The technique is to trade in minimum fluctuations, taking small profits and losses on a heavy volume of trades.

♦ Spreaders watch the markets and note the shifting price relationships between different delivery months of the same commodity, between the prices of the same commodity traded on different exchanges, between the prices of different but related futures contracts, or between cash and futures prices of the same commodity. In each case, there are normal relationships that exist from month to month, reflecting usual market situations. When those price relationships vary from their usual patterns, spreaders sell the overpriced market and buy the underpriced market.

♦ Leverage is an attractive feature of the futures market for speculators because it enables them to control the full value of a futures contract with relatively little capital. This capital requirement (performance bond margin) is not a down payment for the futures contract; rather, it is a security deposit to ensure contract performance. If the market moves against the position, the speculator will be required to deposit additional margin. And if the market moves in favor of the position, his account will be credited.

♦ When speculating in futures markets, it is important to develop a trading strategy or plan to guide market activity.

Take the time to test your speculating knowledge by answering the following questions. After taking the test, score yourself by referring to the answers at the end of the section. If you have more than four errors, review the material in Section Three and Chapter 9 of the *Commodity Trading Manual* before going on.

Self-Test

Fill-In
Using the list of words below, complete the sentences on the following page.

buy	price risk
capital	scalper
day trader	sell
fundamental analyst	short
liquidity	spreader
long	technical analyst
position trader	trading strategy

1. A speculator expects interest rates to rise. To take advantage of this possible market trend, he would _____ Treasury bond futures contracts.

2. Speculators assume _____ and add _____ and _____ to futures markets.

3. If a speculator expects dry weather conditions during the height of the soybean growing season, he would _____ soybean futures contracts.

4. When the price relationship between two futures contracts varies from usual market situations, a _____ would sell the overpriced market and buy the underpriced market.

5. When speculating in the futures markets, it is important to develop a _____.

6. If a speculator is _____ futures, then he has purchased one or more futures contracts; if a speculator is _____ futures, then he has sold one or more futures contracts.

Short Answer

Answer each of the following questions with a word, phrase, sentence, or paragraph.

7. A grain speculator has been following the corn market and notices that futures prices have been relatively low for several months. It is early February and he expects there will be heavy participation in the government farm program for corn, which would reduce the number of acres planted to corn this coming spring.

   A. Based on these two facts, do you anticipate the speculator would buy or sell corn futures contracts?

   On February 3, the speculator takes a position in December corn futures at $1.75/bushel. On March 15, the government announces a high participation rate in the corn farm program. Subsequently, December corn futures rally to $1.93/bushel.

   B. Based on the speculator's first position in the futures market, how much has he gained or lost per contract? (One CBOT corn futures contract equals 5,000 bushels.)

   C. On July 15, the speculator reevaluates his position. There has not been much rain in the Midwest during the past six weeks. World demand for U.S. corn has increased. December corn futures are now trading at $1.98/bushel. How much per contract has the speculator gained or lost since March 15?

D. On July 15, how much has he gained or lost per contract since February 3?

E. How would the speculator offset his initial position?

8. Assume a speculator has been studying the Treasury bond market for several months. During that time, prices have been at record highs. The Federal Reserve then decides to increase the discount rate, making borrowing money more expensive to commercial banks and, subsequently, causing interest rates to rise.

A. Based on this information alone, should the speculator buy or sell T-bond futures contracts?

On March 1, a speculator initiates a position in June T-bond futures at 86-00. Then, on March 23, the Federal Reserve sells Treasury bonds, thus reducing the supply of money available for lending. June T-bond futures are now trading at 82-00.

B. Based on his first step in the futures market, how much has the speculator gained or lost per contract since March 1? (One CBOT T-bond futures contract equals $100,000 face value U.S. Treasury bonds.)

C. How would he offset his original position?

9. Weather reports indicate abnormally high rainfall for the next two weeks as the wheat harvest approaches. A speculator believes this could cause wheat prices to rise and decides to buy four July wheat contracts at $2.60/bushel. (One CBOT wheat futures contract equals 5,000 bushels.)
   The weather predictions prove to be accurate, with heavy rains delaying harvest and driving prices up to $2.70. The speculator expects wheat prices to move still higher. However, he decides to offset two contracts at $2.70 and hold on to the other two long positions in case prices rally further. The prices continue to rise slightly. Later the market drops to the $2.67 range. The trader offsets his position and sells the remaining July wheat contracts at $2.67.

A. How much did he make on the first two wheat contracts he offset?

B. What was the gain on the remaining two contracts that were later offset?

For Further Practice

10. Assume the stock market shows signs of a price decline and the earnings forecast of many blue-chip stocks included in the Major Market Index (MMI) does not look good. Currently, the MMI is near 448.84. The speculator decides to enter the futures market using the November MMI futures contract, which is priced at 448.90. The market turns bearish for a couple weeks and then it looks like a price rally is imminent. At the time, the November MMI futures contract is trading at 445.00 and the speculator decides to offset his position.

    Complete a T-account to show the speculator's first and second steps and his market gain or loss per contract based on his initial position. (A one-point move in the CBOT Major Market Index futures contract equals $250 times the value of the Major Market Index.)

Date	Action
Now	
Later	
Result	

1. **Sell.** When interest rates rise, the price of interest rate futures, such as T-bonds, decreases. To take advantage of this market, a speculator would sell T-bond futures contracts. To offset the position at a later date, the speculator would buy T-bond futures contracts.

2. **Price risk, liquidity, capital.** Speculators in futures markets fulfill several vital economic functions that facilitate the marketing of basic commodities and trade in financial instruments. Most importantly, speculators provide hedgers with vital risk-shifting opportunities, which add liquidity and capital to the market.

3. **Buy.** If rainfall is below normal during the height of the soybean growing season, yields could be down. Low harvest levels could cause prices to rise. To take advantage of this market, a speculator would buy soybean futures contracts. To offset the position at a later date, he would sell soybean futures contracts.

4. **Spreader.** Spreaders watch the price levels between different markets, and when the price relationship varies from their usual patterns, they will sell the overpriced market and buy the underpriced market. If the market moves as expected, the spreader profits from the change in the relationship between the prices of the contracts once he offsets the spread.

5. **Trading strategy.** Successful speculation requires traders to know their limits and develop a trading plan to meet their market objectives.

6. **Long, short.** There are several ways of classifying speculators. The simplest is to refer to speculators as long or short. If a speculator is long futures, then he has purchased one or more futures contracts; if a speculator is short futures, then he has sold one or more futures contracts.

7. A. **He would buy corn futures,** expecting a price rise.

   B. **He has gained $900 per contract** ($1.93 − $1.75 = $.18; $.18 × 5,000 = $900).

   C. **He has gained $250 per contract** ($1.98 − $1.93 = $.05; $.05 × 5,000 = $250).

   D. **He has gained $1,150 per contract** ($1.98 − $1.75 = $.23; $.23 × 5,000 = $1,150).

   E. **Sell (short) the same number of December corn futures contracts initially bought on February 3.**

8. A. **He would sell T-bond futures,** expecting T-bond prices to decline, since interest rates are expected to rise.

   B. **He has gained $4,000 per contract** (86-00 − 82-00 = 4-00, or $4,000).

   C. **Buy (long) the same number of June T-bond futures contracts initially sold on March 1.**

9. A. Long (buys) 2 wheat contracts at $2.60/bushel
      Short (sells) 2 wheat contracts at $2.70/bushel
      $2.70 − 2.60 = $.10/bushel gain, or $500/contract, or a $1,000 total gain ($.10 × 5,000 = $500; $500 × 2 = $1,000)

   B. Long 2 wheat contracts at $2.60/bushel
      Short 2 wheat contracts at $2.67/bushel
      $2.67 − $2.60 = $.07/bushel gain, or $350/contract, or $700 total gain ($.07 × 5,000 = $350; $350 × 2 = $700)

10.

Date	Action
Now	Sells 1 Nov MMI futures contract at 448.90*
Later	Buys 1 Nov MMI futures contract at 445.00*
Result	3.90-point gain × $250 = $975

*The speculator would initially sell futures, since he anticipates a price decline.

SECTION FOUR–PRICE ANALYSIS

The following highlights cover topics presented in Chapter 10 of the *Commodity Trading Manual*. After you've read the chapter, review the highlights below, then try your hand at answering the questions at the end of the section. If you have a problem answering any of them, be sure to reread the material in the CTM.

♦ Two basic trading techniques used by market analysts to forecast price movement in futures markets are fundamental and technical analysis.

Fundamental Analysis

♦ Fundamental analysts (fundamentalists) watch the economic factors that affect supply and demand in attempting to forecast prices and develop profitable trading strategies. They operate on the principle that any economic factor that decreases the supply or increases the use of a commodity tends to raise prices. Conversely, any factor that increases the supply or decreases the use of a commodity tends to increase stocks and lower prices.

♦ Carryover stocks are among the factors most critically watched by fundamentalists trading agricultural futures markets. (Carryover is the amount of grain or oilseed that remains at the end of a marketing year.)

♦ Yield is the amount of grain harvested per acre planted, and it directly affects the attitude and action of buyers in the marketplace.

♦ Monitoring the production of agricultural commodities requires the fundamental analyst to watch the regularly scheduled government and private reports on farm production in the United States and abroad.

♦ Traders monitor the amount of moisture, the time of frost, and the temperature during the growing season and determine their impact on world growing conditions to gauge how crop production is affected around the world.

♦ Domestic and international economic conditions also affect commodity prices.

♦ Other factors fundamental analysts watch regarding agricultural markets include: competition with other commodities, politics, and worldwide competition.

♦ Fundamental price analysis in the financial instrument area involves forecasting the supply of and demand for credit and the price of fixed-income securities.

◆ U.S. monetary policy is formed by the Federal Reserve Bank Board and is administered through the Federal Reserve System. Because the Federal Reserve controls the circulation of money, its policies and actions have a great impact on interest rate levels.

◆ Economic reports released by the U.S. government are excellent sources of financial information. The elements that make up these reports can be grouped into three categories: leading, concurrent, and lagging indicators.

◆ Leading indicators signal the state of the economy for the coming months. They imply possible changes in the business cycle and, as a result, provide the analyst with an early indication of interest rate trends.

◆ Concurrent and lagging indicators show the general direction of the economy and confirm or deny a trend implied by the leading indicators.

◆ The Federal Reserve system provides information that is helpful in analyzing the economy and predicting Federal Reserve activity.

◆ According to price theory, the point where the quantity demanded and the quantity supplied are equal is called the *equilibrium* or *market price*. The purpose of fundamental analysis is to pinpoint and recognize the major factors in the market and to predict their effect on the equilibrium price of a commodity.

◆ Using fundamental analysis involves formulating an economic model—a systematic description of the various supply and demand factors that interact to determine price.

◆ Using computer analysis and modeling techniques to describe in mathematical terms the relationship among economic factors such as interest rates, government policies, and capital is known as *econometrics*.

◆ Traders who prefer to anticipate market movement by studying price patterns in the past using historical prices, trading volume, open interest, and other trading data are called *technicians* and the technique they use to forecast prices is referred to as *technical analysis*.

Technical Analysis

◆ One of the oldest methods of technical analysis is known as *charting*.

◆ Two basic price charts are bar charts and point-and-figure charts.

◆ In a bar chart, the vertical axis represents price and the horizontal axis represents time. Each trading day is represented by a vertical line that connects the lowest and highest price of the day. The day's closing price is indicated by a horizontal bar that crosses the vertical line.

♦ As price data are plotted, technicians begin to see different bar chart formations. Prominent bar chart formations are day, support and resistance, trends, channels, head-and-shoulders, double tops, double bottoms, rounded tops, rounded bottoms, gaps, triangles, flags, and ascending wedges.

♦ Inside day, outside day, closing price, and key reversal are different day formations.

♦ The inside day is one in which the high and low prices of a trading day are within the previous day's price range.

♦ The outside day formation occurs when the high/low prices exceed the previous day's range.

♦ The closing price reversal is a formation in which prices initially continue in the same direction as the previous trading day but reverse to close opposite the previous day's close.

♦ In the key reversal formation, the opening and closing prices exceed the extremes of the previous day's range.

♦ Support is a place on a chart representing where the buying of futures contracts is sufficient to halt a price decline.

♦ Resistance on a chart indicates a price range where selling pressure is expected to stop a market advance.

♦ An uptrend is a sequence of both higher highs and higher lows.

♦ A downtrend is a sequence of lower lows and lower highs.

♦ Channels are chart formations where the lines connecting highs and lows run almost parallel to a trend line.

♦ A head-and-shoulders formation consists of four phases: the left shoulder, the head, the right shoulder, and a penetration of the neckline.

♦ Double tops, double bottoms, rounded tops, and rounded bottoms are chart formations that look exactly as their names suggest.

♦ Gaps in price charts represent a price area where the market did not trade. There are several types of gaps, including the common gap, the breakaway gap, the runaway gap, and the exhaustion gap.

♦ Three triangle patterns are the ascending triangle, the symmetrical triangle, and the descending triangle.

♦ A flag is formed when a substantial upward price move is followed by a modest downward price drift, giving the appearance of a flag on a pole in the absence of wind. An ascending wedge starts the same way, with a significant price trend upward followed by a series of further up days that fail to accelerate as quickly as the initial uptrend.

♦ Point-and-figure charts illustrate trading as one continuous path and ignore time. As with bar charts, the vertical axis of the point-and-figure chart represents price; however, there is no time reference along the horizontal axis. An *x* indicates an uptick and an *o* indicates a downtick.

♦ Traders also try to recognize different price trends through statistical methods known as *statistical analysis.*

♦ One statistical method used by traders is the moving average—an average of a series of prices. There are a variety of moving averages. One example is a three-day average, which is calculated by adding the closing prices from three consecutive days. That total price is then divided by three to determine the first moving-average point. Subsequent moving-average points are calculated the same way—substituting the most recent closing price for the oldest closing price.

♦ An oscillator is a technical indicator that allows a trader to measure overbought or oversold conditions in sideways markets.

♦ Many moving-average and oscillator programs are computerized so technical analysts have this information at their fingertips.

♦ Other tools used by technicians to forecast prices are trading volume, open interest, CFTC reports, contrary opinion, CBOT Market Profile®, and cyclical theories.

♦ Trading volume is the total number of contracts traded for a given time period.

♦ *Open interest* refers to the number of contracts that have been entered into and not yet liquidated by delivery or offset.

♦ The CFTC issues a monthly report showing the total number of open positions held by large-volume traders, speculators, and hedgers, as well as those held by market participants with smaller positions.

♦ The theory of contrary opinion holds that when more than 80 percent of all analysts are bullish, it can be assumed that they and their followers have taken long positions, leaving fewer potential additional buyers to absorb any selling that develops. Conversely, if 80 percent are bearish, the market is likely to become badly oversold.

♦ CBOT Market Profile® is an information service that helps technical traders analyze price trends and consists of a Time and Sales quotation ticker and the Liquidity Data Bank (LDB)®.

♦ Cyclical theories are based on the premise that in nature certain phenomena have cycles, and some analysts use this theory in forecasting price. One cyclical, or wave, theory is the Elliot Wave Principle.

♦ While there are purists of each technique, many traders use a combination of fundamental and technical methods to forecast price. But, no matter which method or combination of methods for price analysis is used, none can be taken as foolproof.

Self-Test

Take the time to test your knowledge of different price forecasting methods by answering the following questions. After taking the test, score yourself by referring to the answers at the end of the section. If you have more than four errors, review the material in Section Four and Chapter 10 of the *Commodity Trading Manual* before going on.

Fill-In

Using the list of words below, complete the following sentences.

bar	head-and-shoulders
bearish	inflation
bullish	moving average
carryover stocks	open interest
channel	point-and-figure
common gap	resistance
downtrend	runaway gap
econometrics	support
equilibrium	technical analysts
exhaustion gap	trading volume
fundamental analysts	uptrend
futures	

1. In a(n)_____ chart, xs and os indicate upward and downward price movement.

2. _____ is a place on a chart representing where the buying of futures contracts is sufficient to halt a price decline.

3. _____ watch the economic factors that affect supply and demand in attempting to forecast prices and develop profitable trading strategies. _____ believe that prices can be projected based on historical price movement and current market activity.

4. According to price theory, the point where the quantity in demand and the quantity supplied are equal is called the _____ price.

5. The theory of contrary opinion maintains that when more than 80 percent of market analysts are _____, it can be assumed that they and their followers have taken long positions.

6. _____ of agricultural commodities are among the factors most critically watched by fundamentalists.

7. Using computer analysis and modeling techniques to describe in mathematical terms the relationship among economic factors such as interest rates, government policies, and capital is known as _____.

8. A(n) _____ is a sequence of lower lows and lower highs. A sequence of higher highs and higher lows is known as a(n) _____.

Multiple Choice
Select the best answer for the following questions.

9. A technician could use which price-forecasting tool?
   A. Bar chart
   B. CBOT Market Profile®
   C. Moving average
   D. All of the above

10. An outside day formation occurs when:
   A. The high and low prices for the day are within the range of the previous day
   B. The prices proceed in an established direction, but close lower than the previous day
   C. The high and low prices exceed the previous day's range
   D. The high and low prices for the day exceed the range of the previous day, but the close is in a different direction

Short Answer
Answer each of the following questions with a word, phrase, sentence, or paragraph.

11. What factors would a fundamentalist watch to forecast corn prices?

12. What factors would a fundamentalist watch to forecast U.S. Treasury bond prices?

13. Is it possible to combine fundamental and technical trading methods to forecast price?

Problems

Calculate a moving-average chart from the following data:

14. A. On day 1, December corn futures closed at $2.01; the second day, the close was $2.02½; and the third day's close was $2.05½. What is the first point on the three-day moving-average chart?

    B. Continue to calculate the averages from day 4 through day 9 using the following information.

	Day 4	Day 5	Day 6	Day 7	Day 8	Day 9
High	$2.08	$2.10	$2.08	$2.07	$2.04	$2.03
Low	$2.06	$2.08	$2.06	$2.05	$2.02	$2.01
Close	$2.07	$2.08½	$2.07	$2.03¼	$2.06¼	$2.01¾

1. **Point-and-figure.** Point-and-figure charts illustrate all trading as one continuous path and ignore time. The vertical axis represents price and there is no time reference along the horizontal axis. Generally, point-and-figure chartists set their price objective by counting the *xs* (upticks) and *os* (downticks) of specific chart formations.

2. **Support.** With this type of chart formation, a price decline is stopped due to buying pressure.

3. **Fundamental analysts, technical analysts.** The trader who uses fundamental analysis watches the economic factors that affect supply and demand in attempting to forecast prices and develop profitable trading strategies. Technical analysts, on the other hand, prefer to anticipate market movement by studying current and past price patterns.

4. **Equilibrium.** The purpose of fundamental analysis is to recognize and pinpoint the major factors in the market and to predict their effect on the equilibrium price of a commodity.

5. **Bullish.** According to this theory, when more than 80 percent of all market analysts are bullish, it can be assumed that they and their followers have taken long positions, leaving fewer potential additional buyers to absorb any selling that develops. Conversely, if 80 percent are bearish, the market is likely to become badly oversold.

6. **Carryover stocks.** Carryover, the amount of grain or oilseeds that remains at the end of a marketing year, indicates the tightness of supply. A tight supply would be reflected in higher prices, while an ample supply would lower prices.

7. **Econometrics.** While fundamentalists can use computer analysis and modeling techniques to anticipate future price movements, this trading system still requires a measure of judgment, since data fed into the computer must be weighted as to their particular significance.

8. **Downtrend, uptrend.** A downtrend is a sequence of lower lows and lower highs and is considered to be intact until a previous rally is surpassed. Conversely, an uptrend is a sequence of both higher highs and higher lows and is considered to be intact until a previous low point is broken.

9. **D.** Bar charts, moving averages, and CBOT Market Profile® can be used by a technician to study price patterns and anticipate future price movement.

10. **C.** An outside day formation occurs when the high/low prices exceed the previous day's range.

11. **Carryover, yield, agricultural reports, weather, economic conditions, competition with other commodities, politics, and worldwide competition** are among the economic factors a fundamentalist who is trading corn futures would watch.

12. **Federal Reserve actions and their effect on money supply; leading, concurrent, and lagging indicators; and government reports** are just a few of the factors a fundamentalist trading T-bond futures would watch.

13. **Yes.** Traders frequently use a combination of fundamental and technical methods to forecast price. For example, many traders obtain a forecast of price movement using fundamental analysis and then choose the time for initiating or liquidating a position on the basis of technical factors. But, no matter which method or combination of methods for price analysis is used, none can be taken as foolproof.

14. **A.** To calculate the first point on a three-day moving-average chart, add three consecutive closing prices. That total price is then divided by three to determine the first moving-average point.
   $2.01 + 2.02½ + 2.05½ = $6.09
   $6.09 ÷ 3 = $2.03

   B. To calculate succeeding points in a moving-average chart, substitute the next closing price for the oldest closing price and proceed as before.

	Closing Prices Used		Total	Average
Day 4	$2.02½ + 2.05½ + 2.07	=	$6.15	$2.05
Day 5	$2.05½ + 2.07 + 2.08½	=	$6.21	$2.07
Day 6	$2.07 + 2.08½ + 2.07	=	$6.22½	$2.07½
Day 7	$2.08½ + 2.07 + 2.03¼	=	$6.18¾	$2.06¼
Day 8	$2.07 + 2.03¼ + 2.06¼	=	$6.16½	$2.05½
Day 9	$2.03¼ + 2.06¼ + 2.01¾	=	$6.11¼	$2.03¾

SECTION FIVE—SPREADING

The following highlights cover topics presented in Chapter 11 of the *Commodity Trading Manual*. After you've read the chapter, review the highlights below, then try your hand at answering the questions at the end of the section. If you have a problem answering any of them, be sure to reread the material in the *CTM*.

♦ A *spread* refers to the simultaneous purchase and sale of two different futures contracts.

♦ When establishing or putting on a spread, a trader looks at the price relationship between contracts rather than the absolute price levels. The contract that is viewed as "cheap" is purchased while the contract that is viewed as "expensive" is sold. If market prices move as expected, the trader profits from the change in the relationship between the prices of the contracts.

♦ The economic contributions of spreading are twofold: (1) spreading restores prices to more normal relationships following a distortion in those relationships, and (2) it provides market liquidity.

♦ Spread orders may specify prices at which the long or short positions should be put on, or the price difference at which the spread should be established.

♦ Spreads are quoted as the price difference between two related contracts. As an example, to calculate a particular agricultural spread such as the July/November soybean spread, one would subtract the price of the November contract from the July contract.

♦ For the spread between two contracts to change, such as July soybeans to gain on November soybeans, there are four possible market scenarios: (1) in a bull market, July soybeans rise faster than November soybeans, (2) in a bear market, July soybeans fall slower than November soybeans, (3) July soybeans remain unchanged while November soybeans fall, or (4) July soybeans rise while November soybeans remain unchanged.

♦ Those who trade spreads do so for two important reasons—lower risk and attractive margin rates.

Interdelivery (Intramarket) Spreads

♦ An interdelivery (or intramarket) spread is defined as the purchase of one delivery month of a given futures contract and the simultaneous sale of another delivery month of the same commodity on the same exchange, e.g., buy CBOT July wheat and sell CBOT December wheat, or sell CBOT December T-bonds and buy CBOT March T-bonds.

♦ An interdelivery spread attempts to take advantage of the price difference between two delivery months of a single futures market when the difference is abnormal or expecting to turn abnormal.

♦ Traders can describe interdelivery spreads as either bull or bear spreads.

♦ In an ag or financial bull spread, a trader buys the nearby and sells the deferred, expecting the nearby to gain on the deferred. This is referred to as *buying the spread*.

♦ In an ag or financial bear spread, a trader sells the nearby and buys the deferred, expecting the deferred to gain on the nearby. This is referred to as *selling the spread*.

♦ Another common interdelivery spread is a butterfly spread. A butterfly spread involves the placing of two interdelivery spreads in opposite directions with the center delivery month common to both spreads. An example of a butterfly spread is: short 3 March T-bonds/ long 6 June T-bonds/short 3 September T-bonds.

♦ Among storable commodities, such as grains and metals, carrying charges have the greatest effect on the underlying futures prices of different delivery months.

♦ Theoretically, in a normal agricultural futures market—reflecting adequate supplies of the underlying cash commodity, normal demand, and sufficient storage capacity—the price of the nearby futures month and the price of the deferred futures month have a definite price relationship. The deferred futures price is usually more than the nearby futures price by approximately the amount of the cost of carrying the commodity from the nearby to the deferred month.

♦ In periods when an agricultural commodity is in short supply, the nearby futures contract trades at a premium to the deferred futures. Such a market is called an *inverted market*.

♦ A common interdelivery spread in the ag markets is the intercrop, or old-crop/new-crop, spread. It involves buying futures in one crop year and selling futures in another crop year. Since prices are usually lowest at harvest—reflecting large, new supplies coming to market—new-crop futures tend to be priced lower than futures from the previous crop year.

♦ With interest rate futures, the cost of carry is determined by the differential between the yield on the cash instrument under consideration and the cost of funds necessary to buy the instrument.

♦ Financial traders watch the relationship between short- and long-term interest rates and, depending upon their market expectations, will decide whether or not to put on a spread.

Intermarket Spreads

♦ An intermarket spread is defined as the sale of a given delivery month of a futures contract on one exchange and the simultaneous purchase of a futures contract of the same delivery month and commodity on another exchange, e.g., sell CBOT December wheat and purchase KCBT December wheat, or buy CBOT MMI futures and sell CME S&P 500 futures.

♦ Different factors that can affect the price difference between markets include: transportation costs, class and grade of a commodity, or maturity of a financial instrument deliverable on an exchange.

♦ In the futures markets, an intermarket spread is often loosely referred to as *arbitrage*—the purchase and sale of similar commodities in two different markets to take advantage of a price discrepancy, e.g., CBOT gold versus COMEX gold, or CBOT T-bonds versus LIFFE T-bonds. By performing this economic function, arbitrageurs increase the efficiency of the markets by narrowing the gap between bid and offer prices and minimizing price distortions between similar markets.

Intercommodity Spreads

♦ Intercommodity spreads normally are traded between two different, but closely related, futures markets, e.g., buy July wheat and sell July corn, or sell Municipal Bond Index futures and buy T-bond futures.

♦ Within the agricultural markets, the two commodities of an intercommodity spread can be used either interchangeably or have common supply and demand characteristics. Although it is not necessary to spread the same months, it is a common practice.

♦ The wheat/corn spread is a popular intercommodity spread, and involves buying (selling) one or more wheat futures contracts and selling (buying) one or more corn futures contracts of the same delivery month.

♦ A special type of ag intercommodity spread is the crush spread. It is established by purchasing soybean futures and selling soybean oil and soybean meal futures.

♦ To make a profit from soybean processing, soybeans must be purchased at a lower cost than the combined sales income from the finished oil and meal. The difference, or profit margin, is called the *gross processing margin* (GPM).

♦ The crush spread can be used by soybean processing firms to minimize the financial risks of sudden increases in soybean costs and/or declining values of finished soybean oil and meal. Given a favorable price relationship between soybean futures and soybean oil and meal futures, the processor buys soybean futures and simultaneously sells oil and meal futures. He holds the long soybean portion of his hedge until he actually buys the required cash soybeans. The processor holds the short side of his crush spread until he is ready to sell his finished oil and meal.

◆ The opposite of a crush spread is called a *reverse crush*. This spreading opportunity results from distortions in normal price patterns when the cost of soybeans is higher than the combined sales value of soybean oil and meal.

◆ Within the financial markets, the two contracts of an intercommodity spread tend to respond to the same economic and financial factors, may have comparable terms to maturity, and generally have somewhat comparable risk/return relationships.

◆ Two of the most actively traded intercommodity spreads among financial instruments are the MOB (Munis Over Bonds, i.e., munis minus T-bonds) and the NOB (10-year Notes Over Bonds, i.e., notes minus bonds).

Take the time to test your spreading knowledge by answering the following questions. After taking the test, score yourself by referring to the answers at the end of the section. If you have more than four errors, review the material in Section Five and Chapter 11 of the *Commodity Trading Manual* before going on.

Fill-In

Using the list of words below, complete the following sentences.

arbitrage	gross processing margin
bear	intercommodity
bull	interdelivery (intramarket)
butterfly	intermarket
buys	nearby
carrying costs	reverse crush
crush	sells
deferred	

1. A(n) _____ spread is the purchase of one delivery month of a given futures contract and the simultaneous sale of another delivery month of the same contract on the same exchange.

2. The purchase of a given delivery month of one commodity or financial instrument and the simultaneous sale of the same delivery month of a different, but related, commodity or financial instrument is called a(n) _____ spread.

3. When putting on a spread, a trader _____ the contract that is viewed as "cheap" and _____ the contract that is viewed as "expensive."

4. In an ag or financial _____ spread, a trader is long the nearby contract and short the deferred contract.

5. In a(n) _____ spread, a trader sells soybean futures and buys soybean oil and soybean meal futures.

6. A(n) _____ spread involves the placing of two interdelivery spreads in opposite directions with the center delivery month common to both spreads.

Multiple Choice
Select the best answer to each of the following questions.

7. Carrying charges include the cost of:
   A. Interest
   B. Storage
   C. Insurance
   D. All of the above

8. Which is not an example of an intercommodity spread?
   A. Buy July wheat futures and sell July corn futures
   B. Sell Municipal Bond Index futures and buy T-bond futures
   C. Buy December T-bond futures and sell March T-bond futures
   D. Sell November soybean futures and buy December soybean oil and meal futures

9. The wheat/corn spread is an example of:
   A. An intercrop spread
   B. An intercommodity spread
   C. An interdelivery spread
   D. A crush spread

10. If a trader purchased T-note futures and sold T-bond futures, under which scenario would he lose money?
   A. In a bull market, T-note futures rise faster than T-bond futures
   B. In a bear market, T-note futures fall slower than T-bond futures
   C. T-note futures remain unchanged while T-bond futures rise
   D. T-note futures rise while T-bond futures remain unchanged

Short Answer

Answer each of the following questions with a phrase, sentence, or paragraph.

11. What are two reasons why a market participant would trade spreads?

12. How are spreads quoted?

Problems

13. What is the gross processing margin if soybean oil is selling at $13.88 per hundredweight, soybean meal is at $156.50 per ton, and soybeans are at $4.85 per bushel? (To answer this question, you may have to refer to Chapter 13, page 205, in the *Commodity Trading Manual*.)

14. On June 15, a trader anticipates that data scheduled for release in July will show the gross national product to fall, reflecting a slowdown in the economy. In response to this, he expects the Federal Reserve to prompt a decline in interest rates, with the long-term end of the yield curve experiencing the greatest price change (i.e., the trader anticipates the price of T-bonds—long-term financial instruments—to be affected more than T-bills or T-notes).

   If his market expectations come true, he believes the price of the nearby T-bond futures contract will rise faster and with greater magnitude than the price of the deferred month.

   A. Under this market situation, would a trader establish a bull or bear spread?

   Assume the trader established a spread on June 15 when September T-bonds were trading at 98-29 and December T-bonds were trading at 98-22. Then, on July 23, he closed the position when September T-bonds were trading at 99-23 and December T-bonds were trading at 99-10.

   B. Complete the T-account on the next page to show the trader's first and second steps in spreading September and December T-bonds. Be sure to indicate whether he lost or made money on the spread.

Sep Futures	Dec Futures	Spread
Jun 15		
Jul 23		
Result		

15. Assume it is early May and a trader establishes a wheat/corn spread. At the time, December wheat is trading at $3.65 and December corn is trading at $2.55. He expects corn to gain on wheat.

   A. Based on this market scenario, what would be his initial market position?

   In October, December wheat futures are trading at $3.50 and December corn futures are trading at $2.65.

   B. Complete the T-account below to show the trader's first and second steps in spreading wheat and corn futures. Be sure to indicate whether he lost or made money on the spread.

Wheat Futures	Corn Futures	Spread
May		
Oct		
Result		

16. In October, a trader expects the Federal Reserve to raise the discount rate. Such action should prompt an overall increase in interest rates and, consequently, a price decline in all U.S. Treasury instruments. However, the trader expects T-bond prices to be affected the most.

    To take advantage of this possible market situation, the trader puts on a spread using five-year T-notes and T-bonds. At the time, five-year T-notes are yielding 7.9 percent and the December T-note futures price is 100-14; T-bonds are yielding 8.15 percent and the December T-bond futures price is 99-03. When he offsets the position three weeks later, T-notes are yielding 8.13 percent and the December T-note futures price is 99-17; T-bonds are yielding 8.38 percent and the December T-bond futures price is 97-06.

    Based on this information, complete T-account below, showing the trader's first and second position and his gains or losses.

Five-year T-note Futures	T-bond Futures	Spread
Oct		
Nov		
Result		

1. **Interdelivery (intramarket).** An interdelivery spread attempts to take advantage of the price difference between two delivery months of a single futures market.

2. **Intercommodity.** Intercommodity spreads normally are traded between two different, but closely related, futures markets. These markets tend to have a strong price correlation because they respond to the same economic and financial factors.

3. **Buys, sells.** When establishing a spread, a trader looks at the price relationship between contracts rather than the absolute price levels—buying the contract that is "cheap" and selling the contract that is "expensive."

4. **Bull.** In an ag or financial bull spread, a trader buys the nearby and sells the deferred, expecting the nearby to gain on the deferred.

5. **Reverse crush.** The reverse crush spread is just the opposite of a crush spread. This spreading opportunity (reverse crush) results from distortions in normal price patterns when the cost of soybeans is higher than the combined sales value of soybean oil and meal. Under this market situation, a trader could initiate a reverse crush—selling soybean futures and buying soybean oil and soybean meal futures.

6. **Butterfly.** The butterfly spread is a common interdelivery spread and involves placing two interdelivery spreads in opposite directions with the center delivery month common to both.

7. **D.** Carrying charges are the combined costs of storage, insurance, and interest. Among storable commodities, such as grains and metals, carrying charges have the greatest effect on the underlying futures prices of different delivery months.

8. **C.** An intercommodity spread is between two different, but closely related, markets. July wheat/July corn, Municipal Bond Index futures/T-bond futures, and November soybeans/December soybean oil and soybean meal are intercommodity spreads, while December T-bonds/March T-bonds is an interdelivery spread.

9. **B.** The wheat/corn spread is a popular intercommodity spread, and involves buying (selling) one or more wheat futures contracts and selling (buying) one or more corn futures contracts of the same delivery month. An intercrop spread, on the other hand, is a type of interdelivery spread and involves buying futures in one crop year and selling futures in another crop year of the same commodity. A crush spread also is an intercommodity spread—buying soybean futures and selling soybean meal and oil futures.

10. **C.** Since the trader is short T-bond futures, he'd lose money if T-bond prices rise and T-note futures remain unchanged.

11. Those who trade spreads do so for two important reasons—**lower risk and attractive margin rates.**

12. **Spreads are quoted as the price difference between two related contracts.** As an example, to calculate the July/November soybean spread, one would subtract the price of the November contract from the July contract.

13. $ Amount × Conversion Factor

Oil value ($0.1388 × 11)   = $1.5268/bu
Meal value ($156.50 × .024) = +3.7560
Combined sales value   = $5.2828
Less soybean costs   = −4.8500
Gross processing margin   = **$0.43¼/bu**

14. A. **Bull spread.** Since the trader expects the nearby contract month to gain on the deferred contract month, he would purchase the nearby and sell the deferred.

B.

Sep Futures	Dec Futures	Spread
Jun 15 Buys 1 Sep T-bond futures contract at 98-29	Sells 1 Dec T-bond futures contract at 98-22	00-07
Jul 23 Sells 1 Sep T-bond futures contract at 99-23	Buys 1 Dec T-bond futures contract at 99-10	00-13
Result 00-26 or $^{26}/_{32}$ gain 26 × $31.25 = $812.50	00-20 or $^{20}/_{32}$ loss −20 × $31.25 = −$625	00-06

Net gain = $187.50 on the spread
          (6 × $31.25 × 1 contract)

15. A. **Buys December corn futures and sells December wheat futures,** since he expects corn prices to gain on wheat prices.

B.

Wheat Futures	Corn Futures	Spread
May Sells 1 Dec wheat futures contract at $3.65	Buys 1 Dec corn futures contract at $2.55	$1.10
Oct Buys 1 Dec wheat futures contract at $3.50	Sells 1 Dec corn futures contract at $2.65	.85
Result 15-cent gain $.15 × 5,000 = $750	10-cent gain $.10 × 5,000 = $500	$.25

Net gain = $1,250 on the spread
($.25 × 5,000 × 1 contract)

16.

Five-year T-note Futures	T-bond Futures	Spread
Oct Buys 1 Dec T-note futures contract at 100-14	Sells 1 Dec T-bond futures contract at 99-03	01-11
Nov Sells 1 Dec T-note futures contract at 99-17	Buys 1 Dec T-bond futures contract at 97-06	02-11
Result 00-29 or $^{29}/_{32}$ loss 29 × $31.25 = $906.25 loss	01-29 or $^{61}/_{32}$ gain 61 × $31.25 = $1,906.25 gain	01-00

Net gain = $1,000 on the spread
(32 × $31.25 × 1 contract)

Comments: The trader was correct in his expectation of increased rates: yields increased by 23 basis points. However, the increase in long-term yields had a greater impact on the price of T-bonds. The spread between five-year T-notes and T-bonds increased by 1 full point, resulting in a profit on the long spread.

SECTION SIX—OPTIONS

The following highlights cover topics presented in Chapter 12 of the *Commodity Trading Manual*. After you've read the chapter, review the highlights below, then try your hand at answering the questions at the end of the section. If you have a problem answering any of them, be sure to reread the material in the *CTM*.

♦ Options on futures contracts were introduced in October 1982 when the Chicago Board of Trade began trading options on Treasury bond futures. T-bond options were initially offered as part of a government pilot program, and the success of this contract opened the way for options on agricultural futures and other financial futures contracts.

Calls and Puts

♦ There are two types of options: calls and puts.

♦ A call option gives the buyer the right, but not the obligation, to purchase a particular futures contract at a specific price anytime during the life of the option.

♦ A put option gives the buyer the right, but not the obligation, to sell a particular futures contract at a specific price anytime during the life of the option.

♦ The price at which the buyer of a call has the right to purchase a futures contract and the buyer of a put has the right to sell a futures contract is known as the *strike price* or *exercise price*.

♦ Trading in call options is completely distinct from trading in put options. For every call buyer, there is a call seller; for every put buyer, there is a put seller.

♦ Open options positions can be liquidated by: (1) offsetting the option, (2) exercising the option, or (3) letting the option expire.

♦ A long call position is offset by selling back the same call option contract. Conversely, a long put position is offset by selling back the same put option.

♦ If an option seller wants to offset his short position, he buys back an option at the same strike price and expiration date—a specific day preceding the futures contract delivery month.

♦ Only option buyers may exercise the contract, i.e., acquire a futures position at the option strike price.

♦ An option can be exercised on any trading day up to and including its last day of trading, which is usually the day before the actual expiration day of the option.

♦ Once the buyer of a put or call exercises the option, the exchange where the contract is traded records an open futures position for the designated contract month at the strike price in the accounts of the buyer and seller.

♦ An option buyer (option holder) must pay the option seller (option writer) a premium.

♦ The only variable of an option contract is the premium. It is determined on the trading floor of an exchange depending on market conditions, such as supply, demand, and other economic and market variables.

♦ Regardless of how much the market swings, the most an option buyer can lose is the option premium.

♦ Since a seller of an option is assigned a futures position if the option is exercised, his risk is the same as someone who is holding a futures position. Because of this risk, the option seller posts margin to demonstrate his ability to meet any potential contractual obligations.

Option Margin

♦ Following the conclusion of each trading session, each seller's option position is marked-to-market to reflect the gains or losses from a particular trading session. If there is a significant adverse price move, the seller may have to post additional margin before the start of the next day's trading to maintain the open position.

♦ Option margins are set by the exchange where the contract is traded at a level high enough to guarantee the financial integrity of the marketplace without unduly increasing the cost of participation to the investor. During conditions of high price volatility, futures exchanges often raise margins; as price volatility decreases, these margins often are lowered.

♦ Option premium is the sum of intrinsic and time value, which are influenced by volatility, the difference between a strike price and the underlying price, and time to maturity.

Option Pricing

♦ Intrinsic value is the difference, if any, between the market price of the underlying futures and the strike price of an option. A call option has intrinsic value if its strike price is below the futures price. A put option has intrinsic value if its strike price is above the futures price.

♦ Any option that has intrinsic value is referred to as being *in-the-money.*

♦ A call option with a strike price above the current market price is said to be *out-of-the-money.* A put option with a strike price below the current market price is said to be *out-of-the-money.*

♦ When the strike price of any put or call option equals the current market price, the option is said to be *at-the-money.*

♦ Two sensitivity measures associated with an option premium are delta and gamma.

♦ Delta measures how much an option premium changes given a unit change in the underlying futures. Delta often is interpreted as the probability that the option contract will move in-the-money by expiration.

♦ Gamma measures how fast delta changes and is defined as the change in delta given a unit change in the underlying futures price.

♦ In addition to intrinsic value, the other component of option premium is time value. Time value is the amount of money that option buyers are willing to pay for an option in the anticipation that over time a change in the underlying futures price will cause the option to increase in value.

♦ Time value also reflects the price that sellers are willing to accept for writing an option.

♦ In general, the more time remaining until expiration, the greater the time value.

♦ At expiration, an option has no time value; its only value, if any, is intrinsic value.

♦ One option-pricing derivative, theta, measures the rate at which an option value decreases with the passage of time.

♦ Volatility of the underlying commodity is one of the more important factors affecting the value of the option premium.

♦ Volatility measures the change in price over a given time period. It is often expressed as a percentage and computed as the annualized standard deviation of percentage changes in daily prices.

♦ Volatility in the price of the underlying futures contract increases the probability that an option will move in-the-money, thereby increasing the option premium. The more volatile the price of the underlying commodity, the greater the chance of an adverse price move; thus, buyers are willing to pay more, and option sellers facing the risk of exercise require higher premiums.

♦ Vega is a pricing variable that measures the net change in an option premium given a 1 percent change in the volatility based on actual option prices.

♦ Option-pricing models take different variables—intrinsic value, time remaining to expiration, and volatility—into account (as well as other factors such as short-term interest rates) to calculate the theoretical value of an option. These theoretical values may or may not correspond to the actual market values in the pit, but are used by traders as a price gauge.

♦ Different option-pricing models also calculate the value of delta, gamma, theta, vega, and other pricing variables.

♦ One of the most prominent option-pricing models is the Black-Scholes, developed by Fischer Black and Myron Scholes in 1973.

♦ Since a call gives the buyer the right to buy a futures contract at a fixed price, a call option buyer believes futures prices will rise by at least enough to cover the premium he paid. In some situations, a trader might buy a call to establish a maximum price for the future purchase of a cash commodity or to cover a short futures position.

Trading Strategies

♦ Bearing in mind that a put is an option to sell a futures contract at a fixed price, a put option buyer expects futures prices to decline by enough to cover the premium. In many cases, a market participant might buy a put to establish a minimum price for the future sale of a cash commodity or to cover a long futures position.

♦ The primary reason for a trader to sell either a call or put option is to earn the option premium.

♦ Generally, call options are sold by individuals who anticipate either little price movement or a slight decrease in prices. In any case, they hope the underlying futures price will not rise to a level that will cause the option to be exercised and result in a loss greater than the premium received.

♦ Those who sell put options generally expect prices to stay the same or increase only slightly. Sellers of put options hope the underlying futures price will not fall to a level that will cause the option to be exercised and result in a loss greater than the premium received.

♦ While some option strategies can be as simple as either buying or selling one option, option strategies can become quite complicated and incorporate a combination of long and short options and/or futures and cash positions. Many of the more complicated option strategies fall under the category of spreads.

◆ An option spread is the simultaneous purchase and sale of one or more options contracts, futures, and/or cash positions.

◆ Since the prices of two different contracts for the same or related instruments have a tendency to move up or down together, spread trading can offer protection against losses that arise from unexpected or extreme price volatility. This occurs because losses from one side of a spread are more or less offset by gains from the other side of the spread.

◆ Other reasons for trading option spreads are: to capitalize on a market environment where one option is overvalued or undervalued in relation to another, to hedge, or to enhance the return on investments.

◆ Vertical spreads, sometimes referred to as *money spreads*, offer traders limited return with limited risk. They involve buying and selling puts or calls of the same expiration month but different strike prices.

◆ Four types of vertical spreads are: (1) bull put spread (long a put at one strike price and short a put at a higher strike price); (2) bull call spread (long a call at one strike price and short a call at a higher strike price); (3) bear put spread (short a put at one strike price and long a put at a higher strike price); and (4) bear call spread (short a call at one strike price and long a call at a higher strike price).

◆ Bull option spreads are used when the trader expects a rising market. Bear option spreads are used when the trader expects a declining market.

◆ Horizontal spreads, also known as *calendar spreads*, offer traders the opportunity to profit from different time decay patterns associated with options of different maturities. Horizontal spreads involve the purchase of either a call or put option and the simultaneous sale of the same type of option with typically the same strike price but with a different expiration month. Because time value in a near-term option decays more rapidly than time value in a more distant option, a near-term option is often sold the same time a distant option is bought.

◆ Horizontal spreads using calls often are employed when the long-term price expectation is stable to bullish. Horizontal spreads using puts often are employed when the long-term price expectation is stable to bearish.

◆ With a conversion, the trader buys a put option, sells a call option, and buys a futures contract. Both options have the same strike price, generally close to the current futures price level, and the same expiration month. The futures contract has the same expiration month as the options.

♦ In a reverse conversion, the trader buys a call option, sells a put option, and sells a futures contract. The put and call options have the same strike price, generally close to the current futures price level, and the same expiration month. The futures price also has the same expiration month as the options.

♦ Delta-neutral spreads, also known as *neutral* or *ratio hedges*, involve offsetting the profit/loss potential in one option position with that in one or more options/futures/cash positions.

Take the time to test your options knowledge by answering the following questions. After taking the test, score yourself by referring to the answers at the end of the section. If you have more than four errors, review the material in Section Six and Chapter 12 of the *Commodity Trading Manual*.

Fill-In

Using the list of words below, complete the following sentences.

above
at-the-money
below
buyers
call option
conversion
exercise
expiration
holder
horizontal
in-the-money

intrinsic value
out-of-the-money
premium
put option
reverse conversion
sellers
staying power
strike
time value
vertical
volatility

1. The _____ or _____ price is the price at which a put or a call option can be exercised by the option buyer.

2. A(n) _____ gives the buyer the right, but not the obligation, to assume a long futures position at a specific price anytime during the life of the option.

3. Option premium is the sum of _____ and _____.

4. If a seller of a call option wants to offset his short position, he buys back a(n) _____ at the same strike price and expiration date.

5. Option _____ do not have to post margin, while option _____ are required to post margin.

6. At _____, an option has no time value; its only value, if any, is intrinsic value.

7. A put option is _____ if the strike price is below the underlying futures price.

8. A call option is in-the-money if the strike price is _____ the underlying futures price.

9. _____ spreads involve the purchase of either a call or put option and the simultaneous sale of the same type of option with typically the same strike price but with a different expiration month.

10. A(n) _____ gives the buyer the right, but not the obligation, to assume a short futures position at a specific price anytime during the life of the option.

Short Answer

Answer each of the following questions with a phrase, sentence, or short paragraph.

11. How does volatility affect the price of an option?

12. In general, does the buyer of a call option expect prices to remain stable, to turn bullish, or to turn bearish?

13. In general, does the buyer of a put option expect prices to remain stable, to turn bullish, or to turn bearish?

14. Explain why a trader would sell either a call or put option.

Problems

15. Assume a hedger wants to establish a minimum selling price for his wheat several months before his scheduled delivery date in June. He also wants to take advantage of higher wheat prices if the market rallies between now and June. To meet these objectives, he buys a $4 July wheat put for 20 cents in March. The expected local basis in June is 10 cents under July wheat. In June when the farmer delivers his wheat at the local grain elevator, the basis is 10 cents under July futures, which

are at $3.60, and the $4 July wheat put is trading at 43 cents. Based on this information, answer the following questions:

A. What is the expected selling price for wheat?

B. In June, how much of the option premium is intrinsic value and how much is time value?

C. What is the actual selling price for wheat in June?

D. What would the actual selling price be if July futures are at $4.50 and the basis is 10 cents under July when the wheat is delivered?

16. A financial institution is holding $1 million face value of the current cheapest-to-deliver Treasury bond. Interest rates have been relatively flat and the manager expects them to remain flat over the next several weeks. He would like to create additional income to the portfolio if interest rates remain stable; however, he also would like some protection if interest rates rise.

   To meet these objectives, the manager sells at-the-money T-bond calls. At the time, T-bond futures are priced at 92-00 and the 92-00 calls are trading at 2-32 (2 $\frac{32}{64}$), or $2,500. Based on this information, answer the following questions:

A. If interest rates remain stable between the time the calls are sold and expiration, how much will he make or lose per option sold?

B. If interest rates fall between the time the calls are sold and expiration, how much will he make or lose per option sold?

C. If interest rates rise between the time the calls are sold and expiration, how much will he make or lose per option sold?

1. **Strike, exercise.** The price at which the buyer of a call has the right to purchase a futures contract and the buyer of a put has the right to sell a futures contract is known as the *strike price* or *exercise price*.

2. **Call option.** There are two types of options—calls and puts. A call option gives the buyer the right, but not the obligation, to buy the underlying futures contract at the option's strike price anytime before the call expires.

3. **Intrinsic value, time value.** In general, an option premium is the sum of intrinsic and time value, which are influenced by volatility, the difference between a strike price and the underlying futures price, and time to maturity.

4. **Call option.** Trading in call options is completely distinct from trading in put options. For every call buyer, there is a call seller; for every put buyer, there is a put seller. If someone sells a call option, his short position can be offset by purchasing a call option with the same strike price and expiration date.

5. **Buyers, sellers.** The most an option buyer can lose is the option premium. Because of this limited and known risk, option buyers are not required to maintain margin accounts. Option sellers, on the other hand, face similar risks as participants in the futures markets. They must post margin to demonstrate their ability to meet any potential contractual obligations.

6. **Expiration.** When an option approaches expiration, its time value erodes faster (all else being equal) because there is less time for the option to move in-the-money. At expiration, an option has no time value.

7. **Out-of-the-money.** A put option has no intrinsic value (i.e., it is out-of-the-money) if its strike price is below the underlying futures price.

8. **Below.** Any option that has intrinsic value is referred to as being in-the-money. Intrinsic value is the difference, if any, between the market price of the underlying futures contract and the option's strike price. In the case of a call option, if its strike price is below the futures price, the call is in-the-money.

9. **Horizontal.** Also known as *calendar spreads*, horizontal spreads offer traders the opportunity to profit from different time decay patterns associated with options of different maturities. Because time value in a near-term option decays more rapidly than time value in a more distant option, a near-term option is often sold at the same time a distant option is bought.

10. **Put option.** There are two types of options—calls and puts. A put option gives the buyer the right, but not the obligation, to sell the underlying futures contract at the option's strike price anytime before the put expires.

11. **Increases in volatility cause option premiums to rise.** That is because there is a greater chance that an option will move in-the-money, which will increase the option premium. The opposite is also true: decreases in volatility reduce option premiums.

12. **Bullish.** Since a call gives the buyer the right to buy a futures contract at a fixed price, a call buyer believes futures prices will rise by at least enough to cover the premium paid. In some instances, a trader might buy a call to establish a maximum price for the future purchase of a cash commodity or to cover a short futures position.

13. **Bearish.** Since a put option gives the buyer the right to sell a futures contract at a fixed price, a put buyer believes futures prices will decline by enough to cover the premium. In some cases, a market participant might buy a put to establish a minimum price for the future sale of a cash commodity or to cover a long futures price.

14. **One of the primary reasons why traders sell calls or puts is to earn option premium.** Generally, calls are sold by individuals who anticipate either little price movement or a slight decrease in prices. In any case, they hope the underlying futures price will not rise to a level that will cause the option to be exercised and result in a loss greater than the premium received. Put sellers, on the other hand, generally expect prices to stay the same or increase only slightly. Sellers of puts hope the underlying futures price will not fall to a level that will cause the option to be exercised and result in a loss greater than the premium received.

15. A. Expected cash selling price:

Strike price of July put	$4.00/bu
Option cost	−.20
Expected basis	−.10
Expected cash selling price	**$3.70/bu**

The wheat producer will receive at least $3.70/bushel for his wheat even if the futures price falls below $4/bushel, provided the basis is 10 cents under July futures at delivery time. However, if July wheat futures rise above $4, he'll be able to take advantage of the increase, since the put did not lock in a ceiling price.

B. **40 cents intrinsic value and 3 cents time value.** Since futures are at $3.60, the intrinsic value of the put equals 40 cents, i.e., the difference between the option's strike price and the underlying futures price at delivery ($4 − 3.60 = $.40). The remaining 3 cents ($.43 − $.40) represents time value.

C. Actual cash selling price if July wheat futures are $3.60/bu at delivery:

Futures price at delivery	$3.60/bu
Premium earned from selling the put	+.43
Initial cost of buying the put	−.20
Actual basis	−.10
Actual selling price	**$3.73/bu**

D. Actual selling price if futures price is $4.50/bu at delivery:

Futures price at delivery	$4.50/bu
Option expires worthless	.00
Initial cost of buying the put	−.20
Actual basis	−.10
Actual selling price	**$4.20/bu**

As you can see from these examples, the farmer was able to lock in a floor price of $3.70 and at the same time take advantage of a possible price increase if July wheat futures rose above the $4 strike price. In these problems, the expected and actual basis was the same: 10 cents under July futures. If the basis changed from what was expected, the actual cash selling price also would have changed.

Note: The farmer could have offset the option by selling back the $4 July put before the option expired to recover any remaining time value. This would have increased his actual selling price slightly.

16. A. **$2,500 per call sold.** If interest rates remain stable, the portfolio manager will more than likely keep the entire premium earned from selling the calls, since the options will expire worthless.

B. If interest rates fall, then T-bond futures prices will rise. If T-bond futures prices are **between 92-00 and 94-16** (which is the 92-00 strike price plus the 2½-point premium received), **the portfolio manager can expect to keep a portion or all of the premium received; but, if the market moves above 94-16, the calls will likely be exercised against the portfolio manager.** Even though the portfolio manager will lose on his options position if the market surpasses 94-16, the value of the cash portfolio will increase.

C. If interest rates rise, then T-bond futures prices will fall. If T-bond prices fall **below the 92-00 strike price, the options will have no intrinsic value and will expire worthless.** In this situation, the **portfolio manager will likely keep the entire premium, "cushioning" the loss in value of the cash portfolio to 89-16** (which is the 92-00 strike price less the 2½-point premium).

What's important to remember from this strategy is that the portfolio manager creates additional value to the portfolio if bond prices remain within the range of 89-16 to 94-16. He also achieves some downside protection in the event that interest rates rise.

Note: A trader can offset a short options position before the contract expires to reduce his market exposure. He'll still earn a profit from offsetting the short side if the premium received is greater than the premium paid by buying back the option.

FOR MORE INFORMATION

The *Commodity Trading Manual* and the *Commodity Trading Manual Home Study Workbook* are just two of the many texts published by the Chicago Board of Trade designed to help readers learn more about the futures and options on futures markets. If you would like information on other publications available from the Chicago Board of Trade, call or write:

Chicago Board of Trade
Education and Marketing Services Department
Literature Services
141 W. Jackson Blvd.
Chicago, Illinois 60604

1-800-THE-CBOT or 312-435-3558

and ask for the *Publications Catalog: A Guide to CBOT Educational and Marketing Materials.*